IRV COTTLER

I'VE GOT YOU UNDER MY SKINS

Contains the original drum charts of all of the tunes on the CD, plus performance hints and in-studio photos.

CONTENTS

IRV COTTLER, a native Brooklynite who began his professional career at the age of 15 has performed with the bands of Red Norvo, Van Alexander, Claude Thornhill, Tommy Dorsey and Les Brown. In his early 20's he conducted for the ice shows at the New Yorker Hotel. A studio musician at NBC for 30 years, he worked on shows starring such luminaries as Dinah Shore, Milton Berle, Nat King Cole and Flip Wilson. He has also worked for all of the major film studios, including Paramount, Columbia, Universal and Disney and has performed for more than 1,000 movies and TV programs and on more than 2,000 records. Although his career is broad in scope, he is probably best known for his 30 year association with Frank Sinatra.

F R A N K   S I N A T R A

I have been the vocalist, for about fifty years, with orchestras that consisted of as little as three musicians up to a full complement of a philharmonic orchestra, which consisted of 125 musicians.

In any case, to a man, each musician has been an important factor to me. The pianist, who essentially is the solo accompanist from time to time; and who also in a sense helps keep me in tune. The string section and the woodwind players, whose beautiful soaring sounds in the orchestrations, inspire in me new ideas even if I have sung a song dozens of times. For energy itself for rhythmic charts obviously comes from the insistency of the brass and the cadence of the rhythm section. With each of these individuals doing his job during a performance, whether it be live or recording, I have found throughout the years that in the music that I perform, which is obviously the better kind written and orchestrated by the more-talented people than the so-called modern sound, there is a faction upon which I lean more than any other....and that is percussion (or if you wish, the drummer).

Irv Cottler and I have shared thousands of notes, bars, orchestrations, gigs and long talks regarding our labors. Irv has a wonderful faculty of knowing what is the perfect tempo for each chart whether it be a ballad or a rhythm tune. He also has a knack of adding a percussive figure where from time to time an orchestration might have several empty spots. His consistency of tempo prohibits the orchestra from ever straying.

To sum up, listening to this album will give you a complete picture of a man doing his job so well that you have a feeling of comfort, security and never being left out on the hook. He has been and always will be my kind of drummer!

Frank Sinatra

ABOUT THE BOOK AND CD

The book and CD combination of *I've Got You Under My Skins* gives the drummer, or any musician, a chance to see and hear a great, big band drummer in action in the studio.

This book contains the actual drum parts that Irv Cottler used during the recording session. Besides giving you the opportunity to play with the band, they give you an inside look at what is actually written on the drum part. You can look at the parts while listening to how Irv has interpreted them.

Before you sit down at your drumset to play along, spend some time listening to the CD while reading the charts. Pick the first tune you want to work on, and listen to it while focusing on Irv's interpretation. The idea is not to memorize so that you can play what *he* does, but to learn from a master and then develop your own style. Notice how he ignores a brass figure in order to keep the time going or how his ride cymbal beat changes from an open swing feel on up tunes to a tight feel on slower tempos.

Notice how he goes from hi-hat to ride cymbal in "I've Got You Under My Skin." The switch emphasizes the swing feel of the chart. "Fly Me to the Moon" is a great example of playing less and saying more. Remember, the drummer's role is to make the band swing...solo time is later.

The more focused your listening, the more you will learn from this book and CD package. Listen to everything: How the drums are tuned, how fills behind the brass are played on different drums and cymbals than those in back of saxes or piano, etc. But most of all, listen to how Irv Cottler makes the band come to life without ever becoming overpowering. It's no wonder that Frank Sinatra wouldn't use anyone else.

Listen, play and enjoy.

ABOUT THE RECORDING SESSION

I've Got You Under My Skins was recorded live in New York City. Mentioning the fact that the session was "recorded live" may seem unnecessary, but today when so many recordings are layered track by track, when one musician may record on one day and never see another musician who "laid down" his track or another, a full, big band recorded live is a refreshing rarity.

The interaction between the musicians, soloists and arrangers on a live date often creates new ideas which result in adjustments and/or alterations in the charts while the recording session is in progress. All musicians must be very flexible and, of course, attentive so they can quickly adjust their parts.

As you listen to this recording while reading the drum parts, you will see and hear adjustments that took place on the recording date. Since these are the actual drum parts that Irv played on the date, you will see places where he wrote in comments and hear changes that he didn't bother writing in—he simply made a mental note of the changes and played. Following are some examples for you to listen and look for:

Chart 1—The Lady is a Tramp

At 23 the ensemble figures are played both times

At 33—39 the figures were left out the 2nd time

At 39 the figures were played both times

Chart 2—I'll Never Smile Again

Irv left out the 1st bars instead of playing the written ones.

At bar 14 the ensemble figures are played both times.

Irv made the sign (𝄋) bigger so he wouldn't miss it.

Chart 3—Witchcraft

In the 2nd ending after E, the rhythm of the cue in bars 46 and 47 is wrong in Irv's part. We don't know if that was a copying mistake or if Torrie Zito, the arranger/conductor of the date, changed it.

In bars 29, 31, and 33 there is a big ensemble entrance on the "& of one" which isn't indicated on the part.

Chart 5—My Kind of Town

Notice that they slowed down (ritard) in the last bar... it's not written in the part.

Chart 6—I've Got You Under My Skin

Again Irv made the sign (𝄋) bigger.

Chart 7—All or Nothing at All

In bars 20 & 36 there is an ensemble entrance on beat 2.
There is a copying mistake in bar 61. 𝄽 ♩𝄾♩𝄾♪ should be 𝄾 ♩𝄾♩𝄾♪ Irv wrote it in.

Chart 8—This Love of Mine

At bar 24 the figures are played both times.

Chart 9—I Get A Kick Out of You

At bar 57 the figures are played both times.

Chart 10—New York, NY

There were obviously changes in Torrie's mind after they read the chart down. To help start softer and build, he took out the background figures at A the first time through and added piano fills instead.

The ensemble figure, however, which says second time only is played both times.

There is a ritard in bar 68.

What does all this mean? It means a recording drummer has to be able to read, swing and know when to kick and when not to; but he or she should also be a flexible and attentive musician who must think and listen at all times. Don't be afraid to mark your part as you listen. Give yourself cues so when you start to play you will have everything going for you.

DRUMS
1
IRV COTTLER
LADY IS A TRAMP
Arr. by Torrie Zito
Track 1
ENS.
TENOR SX. SOLO 2X
ENS. – TACET 2X
ENS. PLAYS 2X

33
34
35
36
37
38
39
40
(TBN. SOLO)
C
41
42
2
43
44
4
45
46
6
(FILL
(ENS.
47
48
49
50
51
52
1.
53
54
55 - 56
2
2.
57
58
59
60
61
62
63
64
ff

DRUMS
2
IRV COTTLER
I'LL NEVER SMILE AGAIN
Arr. by Torrie Zito
Track 2
ON CUP OF CYM.
ENS.
ENS. (TACET 2X)
TBN. SOLO 2X
SXS PLAY 2X
ENS. PLAYS 2X

DRUMS
2
I'LL NEVER SMILE AGAIN
D
al Coda
ENS.
Tbns
f
ff
TBN SOLO
D.S. al Coda
Coda
TBN SOLO
DICTATED

DRUMS

IRV COTTLER

3

WITCHCRAFT

Arr. by Torrie Zito

Track 3

DRUMS

WITCHCRAFT

D

2 4

29 30 31 32

6

33 34 35 36

E

2 4

37 38 39 40

5

1. (Tpt. Pick up) 2

41 42 43 - 44

2.

45 46 47 48

2

49 50 51 52

53 54 55 56

Piu f

SOLO

57 58

ff

DRUMS

IRV COTTLER

4 FLY ME TO THE MOON

Track 4

Arr. by Torrie Zito

TPT. SOLO AD LIB.

(SXS) mf

A

ENS. - TACET 2X

TENOR SX. SOLO 2X

FILL

f

B

(SXS)

mf

2
FLY ME TO THE MOON
DRUMS
C
ENS. PLAYS 2X
D
1.
ff
2
2.
TEN. SX.
SXS
mf
f
FILL
SXS.
ff
mf
f
FILL
ff

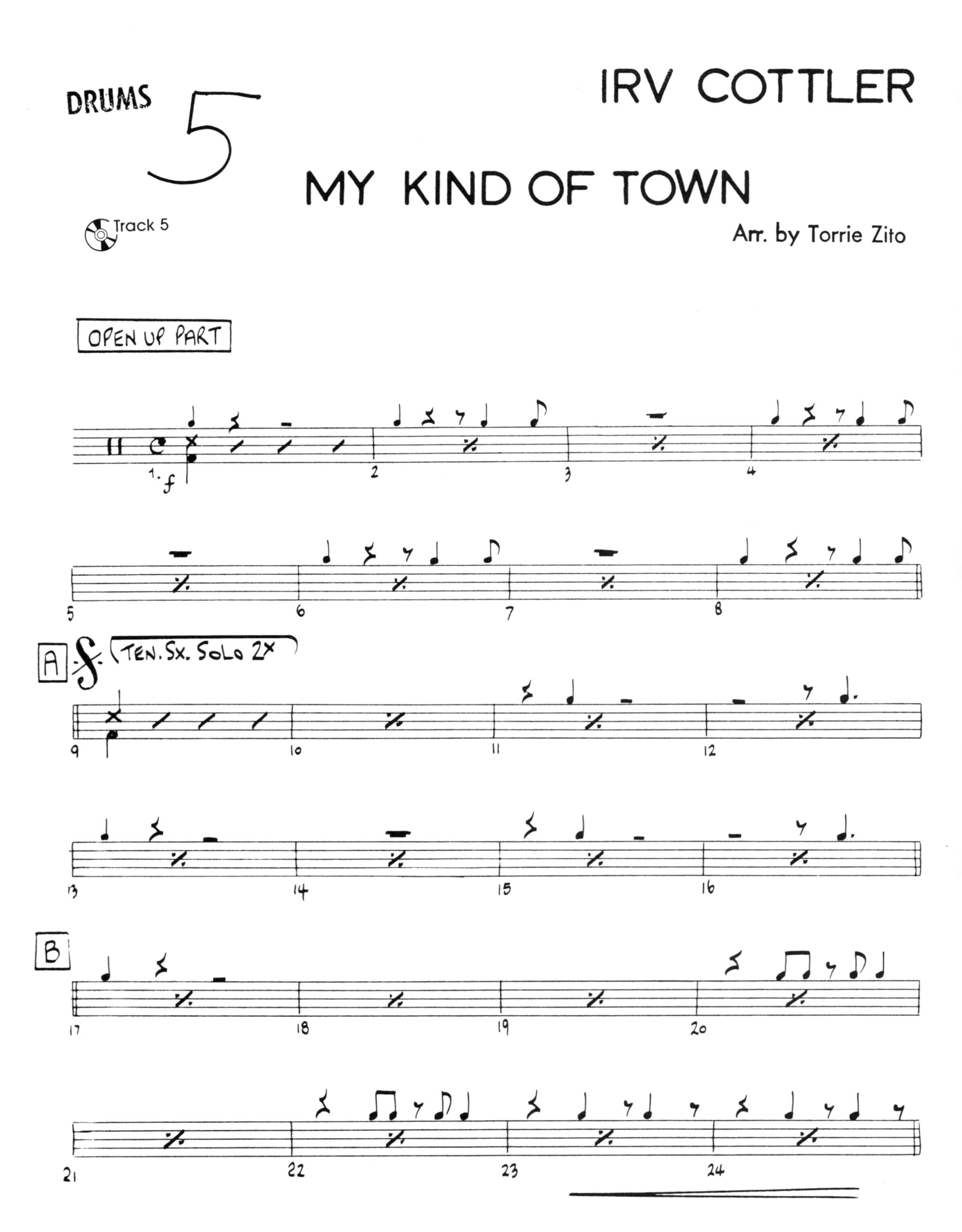
DRUMS
5
IRV COTTLER
MY KIND OF TOWN
Track 5
Arr. by Torrie Zito
OPEN UP PART
A
TEN. SX. SOLO 2X
B

DRUMS

DRUMS

53 54 55 56

G

57 58 59 60

61 62 63 64

H

65 66 67 68

69 70 71 72

I

73 *f* 74 75 76

77 78 79 80

(FILL - - - - - - - - -

81 82

ff

Molto Ritard..
(Slow Down)

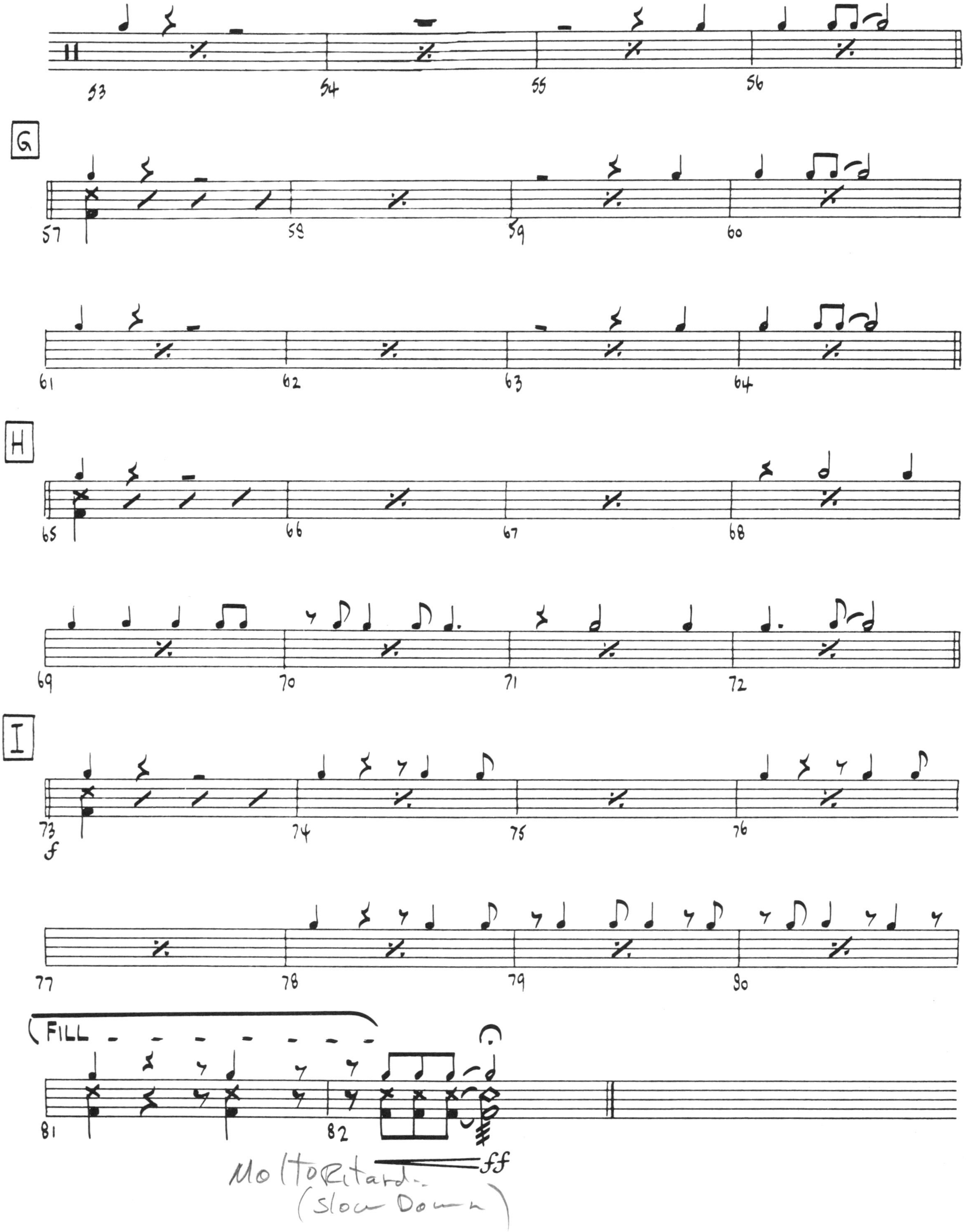

DRUMS

IRV COTTLER
I'VE GOT YOU UNDER MY SKIN

Arr. by Torrie Zito

OPEN UP PART

6

Track 6

DRUMS
2
I'VE GOT YOU UNDER MY SKIN
(4)
(8)
(Sxs.)
C
IN FOUR
Ens.
D
(Tbns
al Coda

DRUMS 3. I'VE GOT YOU UNDER MY SKIN

Irv Cottler serious, but relaxed before the date.

Torrie Zito, arranger extraordinaire, going over a chart with Irv.

Irv snapping off the tempo before a take.

The trumpet section.

DRUMS

IRV COTTLER

ALL OR NOTHING AT ALL

7

Arr. by Torrie Zito

Track 7

DRUMS
2
ALL OR NOTHING AT ALL
B
C

DRUMS
3
ALL OR NOTHING AT ALL
FILL
D
FILL
1.
2
2.
FILL
SOLO
sff

DRUMS

8 IRV COTTLER
THIS LOVE OF MINE

Arr. by Torrie Zito

Track 8

mf f

(Ens.

A (Pno Solo 2×, Ens. Tacet)

(Sxs)

B

2 4

(Tbns

(Ens. Plays 2×

6

C

(Sxs)

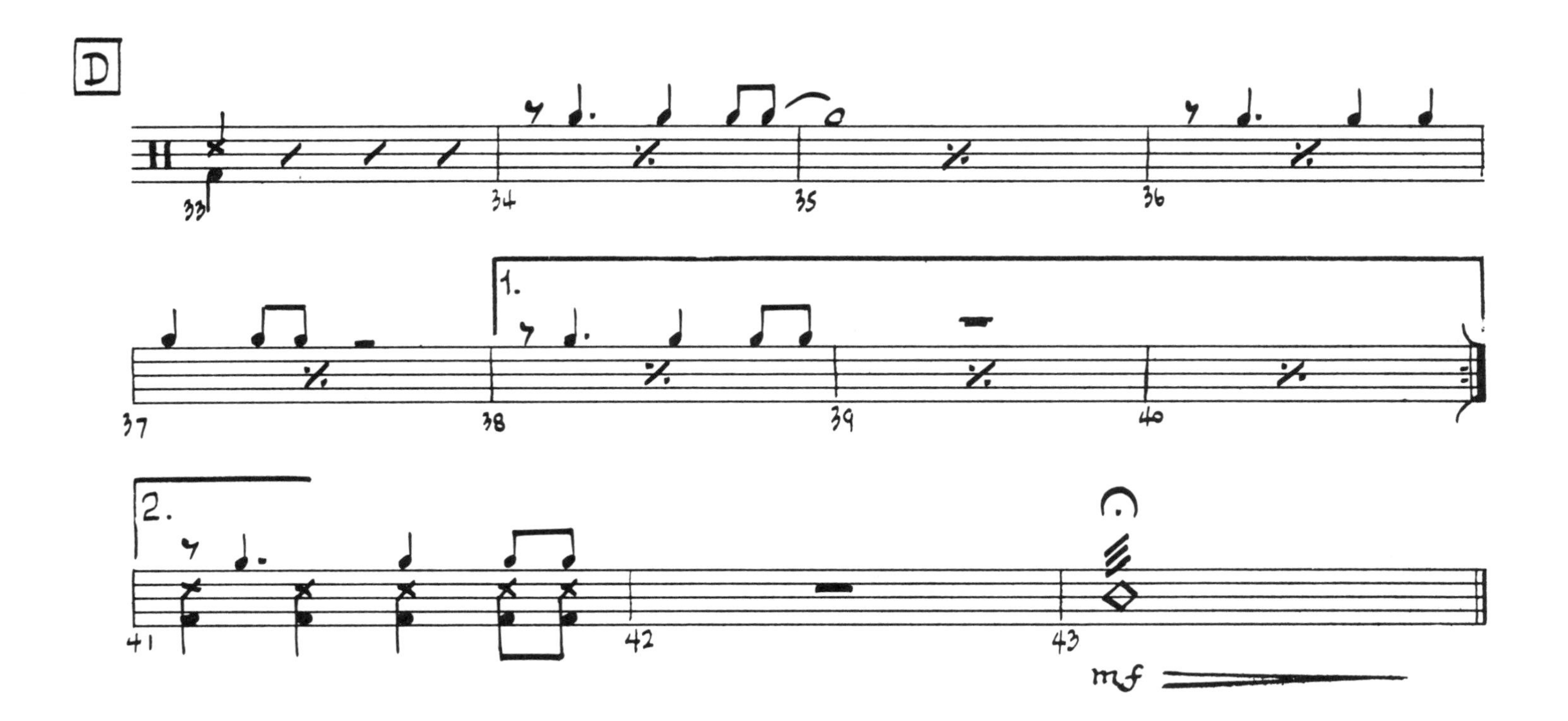
D
33
34
35
36
37
1.
38
39
40
2.
41
42
43
mf

Buddy Rich and Tony Mottola stop in to wish Irv well and listen to a few takes.

The trombone section.

Irv preparing one of those great kicks.

The sax section.

Buddy, Joe Malen, Irv, Ted Sommer, Gene Cherico, hamming it up.

DRUMS

IRV COTTLER

I GET A KICK OUT OF YOU

Arr. by Torrie Zito

DRUMS
2
I GET A KICK OUT OF YOU
B
TBNS
mf
ENS
C
TEN. SX. SOLO 2X
TACET 2X

DRUMS
3
I GET A KICK OUT OF YOU
D
BAND PLAYS 2X
al Coda
D.S. al Coda
Coda
PLAY THRU
SOLO FILL

DRUMS

IRV COTTLER

10 NEW YORK, N.Y.

Arr. by Torrie Zito

DRUMS
2
NEW YORK, N.Y.
E
(Tenor Pick-up)
SXS
D.S. al Coda
Coda
FILL
F
G
FILL

Press Interviews about the Album

HE'S GOT SINATRA UNDER HIS SKIN

by Bruce Fessier
THE DESERT SUN, Palm Springs, California

Ronald Reagan's "trickle-down" philosophy may not be popular with everyone, but it has one definite proponent in part-time Palm Springs resident, Irv Cottler.

Cottler, Frank Sinatra's main drummer for 27 years, has taken advantage of the Voice's almost fanatical following by releasing an album of Sinatra music without Sinatra.

Sinatra's picture is on the album, his words are on the liner notes and Cottler's songs are Sinatra's greatest hits with standard Sinatra arrangements. But The Voice does not sing on the album — nor does any voice for that matter.

It's the type of album where a listener can pretend he's Frank Sinatra and sing along with Old Blue Eyes' band. Instead of Mitch Miller, this is "Sing-along With Irv."

One would think a musical purist would not want to buy this album. It's like the Charlie Parker Quintet without Charlie Parker or the Pips without Gladys Knight. No new musical ground is broken.

But Cottler's album, titled "I've Got You Under My Skin," may appeal to thousands of Sinatra's most devoted fans. It's got some of that Sinatra magic which means some of Sinatra's success just may trickle down to Irv Cottler.

Or at least that's what Cottler's hoping for.

Cottler figured it was about time he cashed in on his lead singer's popularity since hundreds of musicians who weren't associated with Sinatra were making money with music Cottler helped produce.

Cottler determined this after conducting a little marketing study.

"There are 140 albums made on the "Tribute to Sinatra' (theme)," he said, "and do you know what? They all did well."

Sid Mark, a disc jockey from Philadelphia came up with the idea for an album of Sinatra's music without the vocals, and Cottler pursued it.

"Basically, it's my album," said Cottler, who is credited as the producer. "The idea was conceived 10 years ago. We thought about doing an album where people would sing along (with Sinatra's band).

The idea didn't get off the ground, at that time, because Cottler couldn't get the kind of support he wanted from a record producer.

"Ten years ago," he said, "the producers wanted me to do it as a rock album. I couldn't do it. Anyway, with the big band resurgence in the last year or two, I felt it was time."

Now, Cottler said, "the album is getting tremendous reviews all over the country."

"It's unique," said Cottler. "It's recognizable right away. It's got to hit a certain age group — 35 to 55 — and it will go on (selling) for years."

The album is directed at Sinatra fans, but Cottler said it's becoming popular with other groups, as well.

"The idea was to have people sing to it," Cottler said, "but they're also using it back east for exercise classes."

"It's not too far out. People can understand it and people can dance to it."

The title of the album was inspired by a song Sinatra did on his first album with Cottler 27 years ago. That album was titled, "Songs for Swinging Young Lovers" and Cottler was invited to play on it by Nelson Riddle, who Cottler had worked with at the NBC studios.

"Nelson called me up one night," Cottler recalled, "and said, 'We're going to do an album with the Pope.' That was my first album with (Sinatra)."

Cottler remembered what it was like to record it.

"My feeling was of nervousness," he said. "It was Sinatra. I've worked with everybody, but something about this man is just different from every other superstar. The electricity is there."

Cottler started drumming with jazz vibraphonist Red Norvo when Cottler was 17 years old. Later, he played for Van Alexander, Claude Thornhill, Tommy Dorsey and Les Brown.

"Red Norvo, Claude Thornhill and Tommy Dorsey were the greatest teachers you could ever have," said Cottler. "It was like getting a college degree."

He took a job with NBC when he wanted to stay off the road to raise a family, but he did freelance studio work with Sinatra and other musicians throughout the '50s and '60s.

In the early '70s, Cottler became one of Sinatra's five core musicians — the players who record with The Voice and tour with other union musicians who supplement Sinatra's big bands.

"When he came out of retirement 15 years ago," Cottler said, "I went with him exclusively."

His job, as the drummer, was to hold the tempo for Sinatra. But Cottler does more than that. His steady drums embrace Sinatra to the rhythm like a pair of strong seatbelts, giving Sinatra the kind of security he needs to take chances on the vocals and ascend to the heights that have thrilled millions of people.

Cottler, however, is modest about his role with Sinatra. He prefers to credit the singer, whom he calls, "another lead instrument."

"When you say he's another lead instrument," Cottler explained, "he's not really leading (the band), he's adding to it. He's a great natural musician. Tremendous ears."

In their 27-year association, Cottler said Sinatra has never told him, "three words as far as how to play or what to play." But he said the singer expects excellence.

"He expects the same as he gives," said Cottler. "He gives 150 percent and expects the same thing, practically on the same level."

That's not always easy. Since Sinatra rarely sings a song the same way twice, Cottler says he frequently has to "try to outguess" him.

"It's a matter of instinct," he said, "of knowing his moves on stage."

But, despite the difficulty, Cottler said he'd rather play with Sinatra than any other singer.

"I've recorded for everybody, and in the movies, too," said Cottler. "I've worked twice with Barbra Streisand and I think she's one of the greatest who ever lived. But there's still something about Sinatra."

With his new album, Cottler said, "I'm identified with him now more than ever before."

"It's mushroomed," Cottler said, "and I'm really happy about it."

TIME HAS BEEN ON COTTLER'S SIDE

By A. James Liska
Daily News Jazz Critic

He looks like a golfer — tanned face, trim build, plaid pants and open-necked sh
and he speaks frequently and longingly of "getting my golf game together".

His face is gnawingly familiar, remindful of some vague and distant memory, b
ficult to place. His repeated mention of the name Frank turns the head of a guy in th
booth at a West Valley deli, and the connection between Frank Sinatra, the Chairmar
Irv Cottler, the Drummer, becomes clear.

Cottler, whose age is a family and state secret, has been Sinatra's drummer for the p
years. During the last 15 years the onetime NBC staff musician, whose studio schedul
him busy 15 hours a day, six days a week, has worked for nobody else.

As one of the five musicians who forms the nucleus of Sinatra's backup band, C
spends six months a year traveling to the four corners of the world, drums and cymb
tow. Sinatra says Cottler does his job so well "you have a feeling of comfort, securit
never being left out on the hook. He has been and always will be my kind of drum

Those words of praise are from the front cover of Cottler's first non-Sinatra proj
the 15 years since the Chairman came out of retirement, saving Cottler from wh
describes as "a deteriorating music scene" in the studios of Hollywood.

The project is an album — his third ever as a leader — of big band music the way C
— and Sinatra — like it. Though meritorious for its fine musicianship and quality pr
tion, "I've Got You Under My Skins" is pure Sinatra.

Alone with a stereo, the Sinatra fan who knows the words and melodies and has a
imagined himself in the spotlight — dressed in tuxedo, cigarette cupped in hand, drink
nearby piano — can get close to the fantasy.

"That's great! That's what I wanted," says Cottler, a broad smile across his face. "
see, I wanted the arrangements to not be Sinatra's, but be like Sinatra's. I wanted to m
feel like Sinatra is just about ready to sing."

Objective stated, goal accomplished, Cottler settles back to his "lean" corned beef
wich and diet soda to reminisce about his own career and opine about the music bus

"I don't know," he begins, "I'll probably never get the money back that I put int
album, but it's getting airplay at 550 stations around the country. In Philadelphia
Washington it's been rated the best big band.

"We probably could have done better than we're going to," he continues, projectin
sales will be around 35,000 copies. He stops for a moment and shrugs his shoulders.
had all sorts of problems," he adds, waving his hand as if to shoo distribution and co
tual problems aside.

"I've Got You Under My Skins" was conceived by Cottler almost 15 years ago at a
when the record industry was enjoying its heydey. Of course, the industry was prosp
not from big band albums but from rock'n'roll.

"Originally, they wanted me to do the album disco," he says. "I said, 'No Way!

Cottler's musical values were established long before the static rhythms of disco
born. Though he had played for dancers with the bands of Van Alexander, Cl
Thornhill and Tommy Dorsey, the music he helped create was also for listening. A
was not about to change for the sake of a record.

"After all of that," he says, "I decided I would just wait. I ended up doing it — pr
ing it, paying for it — myself."

Born and reared in Brooklyn, N.Y., Cottler began his musical life as a violinist.
child, he was influenced by a cousin who played drums and soon began "fooling aro
with the drums at a neighborhood music store. At 17, he auditioned for his first re
with Red Norvo, the master vibist who, at that time, was still playing xylophone.

"Twenty-five drummers auditioned for that job," Cottler recalls. "Boy, was I nerv
was about the 15th guy to play, and then I got called back for the job. It only lasted a
three months, but it was three months of getting my college degree."

After his stint with Norvo, Cottler began a series of gigs that included being the you
staff drummer at CBS in New York. Big band work with Alexander, Thornhill and D
followed.

"We were on our way to California, following Tommy Dorsey into the Palladium,
Thornhill got his draft notice," Cottler recalls. "I could have enlisted to stay
Thornhill's band, but I decided to stay and play army camps in the states."

By 1947, Cottler had settled in Los Angeles and begun freelancing. In 1951 he b
playing Dinah Shore's 15-minute, daily show. When, in 1953, her show becam
Chevrolet Hour, Cottler became a staff musician for NBC. He also began pursuing
studio gigs.

"We figured out recently that I've done more than 1,000 movies and television prog
and more than 2,000 albums," Cottler says, adding he has done "about 90 percent
Sinatra's LPs over the last 27 years.

"My first date with Sinatra was 'Music for Swinging Young Lovers,'" he says. "I
been working with Nelson Riddle, Billy May and Gordon Jenkins a lot and Nelson c
me to ask if I wanted to do a Sinatra record. I had never worked for him but always wa
to, and figured I could because we had both worked with Dorsey, though I worked for
after Sinatra had already left."

That one date became the first of many, and Cottler began taking leaves from NB
accompany Sinatra on tour. Back at home, he would dig back into the studio trenches
it was time to tour again.

"The studio pressures were very deep and the music was changing. I think there are s
good rock musicians, but for the most part the music being done in the studios wasn't
good. It certainly wasn't my kind of music and when Sinatra announced, about 15 y
ago, that he was coming out of retirement, I received an offer for the gig and
everything else," he says.

The time off gave Cottler the chance to finally get his big-band dream album g
Though he plans to record another big-band record and maybe a combo record wit
Sinatra cohorts, he does not see himself spending six months a year traveling
bandleader.

"They want me to do some gigs back East," Cottler says. "It would be fun and I
bably will do a few gigs here and there, but I really want to get my golf game togeth